THE ALL-TIME GREATES

LOVE COLLEC...

C000260171

❤ PART 1 ❤

Always Bon Jovi
And I Love You So Don McLean
Anyone Who Had A Heart Dionne Warwick
(Everything I Do) I Do It For You Bryan Adams
From Here To Eternity Frank Sinatra
Hard To Say I'm Sorry Chicago
Have I Told You Lately Van Morrison
I Will Always Love You Whitney Houston
Love Is All Around Wet Wet Wet
She Loves You The Beatles
Sometimes When We Touch Dan Hill
That Ole Devil Called Love Alison Moyet
The First Time Ever I Saw Your Face Roberta Flack
To All The Girls I've Loved Before
Julio Iglesias & Willie Nelson
Touch Me In The Morning Diana Ross
Unchained Melody The Righteous Brothers
Until It's Time For You To Go Elvis Presley
When You're Young And In Love Van McCoy
Without You Harry Nilsson

❤ PART 2 ❤

A Woman In Love Barbra Streisand
Always Be My Baby Mariah Carey
Bridge Over Troubled Water Simon & Garfunkel
Could It Be Magic Take That
Falling Into You Celine Dion
For The Good Times Kris Kristofferson
I Am Blessed Eternal
I Can't Stop Lovin' You Don Gibson
I Write The Songs Barry Manilow
Just The Two Of Us Bill Withers
Let's Put It All Together The Stylistics
One Moment In Time Whitney Houston
The Power Of Love Jennifer Rush
This Guy's In Love With You Herb Alpert
To Love Somebody The Bee Gees
Un-Break My Heart Toni Braxton
When You Tell Me That You Love Me Diana Ross
Woman John Lennon
Wonderful Tonight Eric Clapton
Words The Bee Gees

❤ PART 3 ❤

Ain't No Mountain High Enough Diana Ross
All I Have To Do Is Dream The Everly Brothers
An Old Fashioned Love Song Paul Williams
Annie's Song John Denver
Eternal Flame The Bangles
Evergreen Barbra Streisand
Feelings (Dime) Morris Albert
For All We Know The Carpenters
How Deep Is Your Love The Bee Gees
I Feel Fine The Beatles
I Will The Beatles
If You Leave Me Now Chicago
Jealous Guy John Lennon
Killing Me Softly With His Song Roberta Flack
Let's Get It On Marvin Gaye
More Than I Can Say Bobby Vee/Leo Sayer
Oh, Pretty Woman Roy Orbison
Strangers In The Night Frank Sinatra
This Is My Song Petula Clark
Three Times A Lady The Commodores
Your Song Elton John

WISE PUBLICATIONS
London/New York/Paris/Sydney/Copenhagen/Madrid/Tokyo

Exclusive Distributors:
Music Sales Limited
8/9 Frith Street,
London W1B 3JB, England.
Music Sales Pty Limited
120 Rothschild Avenue,
Rosebery, NSW 2018,
Australia.

Order No. AM971795
ISBN 0-7119-9059-X
This book © Copyright 2001 by Wise Publications

Cover design by Chloë Alexander
Photographs courtesy of London Features International
Printed and bound in Malta by Interprint Limited.

Your Guarantee of Quality
As publishers, we strive to produce every book to the highest commercial
standards. This book has been carefully designed to minimise awkward page
turns and to make playing from it a real pleasure. Particular care has been
given to specifying acid-free, neutral-sized paper made from pulps which
have not been elemental chlorine bleached. This pulp is from farmed
sustainable forests and was produced with special regard for the
environment. Throughout, the printing and binding have been planned to
ensure a sturdy, attractive publication which should give years of enjoyment.
If your copy fails to meet our high standards, please inform us and we will
gladly replace it.

Music Sales' complete catalogue describes thousands of titles and is available
in full colour sections by subject, direct from Music Sales Limited.
Please state your areas of interest and send a cheque/postal order for £1.50
for postage to: Music Sales Limited, Newmarket Road, Bury St. Edmunds,
Suffolk IP33 3YB.

www.musicsales.com

PART ONE

Contents

Always

Words & Music by Jon Bon Jovi

1. This Ro-me-o is bleed-ing
(Verse 2 see block lyric)

but you can't see his blood,—

it's no-thing but some feel-ings that this old— dog kicked up.——

Well there

ain't no luck in these load-ed dice— but ba-by if you give me just one more try,— we can

D.%. al Coda

pack up our old dreams and our old lives,— we'll find a place— where the sun still shines yeah.—

Verse 2:

Now your pictures that you left behind
Are just memories of a different life
Some that made us laugh, some that made us cry
One that made you have to say goodbye.

What I'd give to run my fingers through your hair
To touch your lips, to hold you near
When you say your prayers
Try to understand, I've made mistakes, I'm just a man.

When he holds you close, when he pulls you near
When he says the words you've been needing to hear
I'll wish I was him, 'cause those words are mine
To say to you till the end of time.

Anyone Who Had A Heart

Words by Hal David
Music by Burt Bacharach

Very slowly

An-y-one who e-ver loved __ could look at me _____ and know that I love you.

An-y-one who e-ver dreamed _ could look at me _____ and know I dream of you,

And I Love You So

Words & Music by Don McLean

How lone - ly life has been,
But life be - gan a - gain,
And once a page is read,
All but love is dead,

The day you took my hand.
That is my be - lief.
And, yes, I

know how lone - ly life can be,
(love - less)
The shad - ows fol - low

me and the night won't set me free. But I don't

From Here To Eternity

Words by Robert Wells
Music by Fred Karger

(Everything I Do) I Do It For You

Words by Bryan Adams & Robert John 'Mutt' Lange
Music by Michael Kamen

you're there all the time, _____ all the way ___ yeah. _____

Oh you can't

tell me it's not worth try - in' for, I can't

help _____ it, there's no - thin' I want more. Yeah ___ I would

VERSE 2:
Look into your heart
You will find there's nothin' there to hide
Take me as I am, take my life
I would give it all, I would sacrifice.

Don't tell me it's not worth fightin' for
I can't help it, there's nothin' I want more
You know it's true, everything I do
I do it for you.

25

Have I Told You Lately

Words & Music by Van Morrison

There's a love that's di - vine___ and it's yours and it's mine,___ like the

sun___

at the end of the day_____ we should give thanks and pray to the

one.   (3,5.) Have   I

VERSE 2:
Oh the morning sun in all its glory
Greets the day with hope and comfort too
And you fill my life with laughter
You can make it better
Ease my troubles that's what you do.

VERSE 3: — as Verse 1

VERSE 4: — Instrumental

MIDDLE:
There's a love that's divine
And it's yours and it's mine
And it shines like the sun
At the end of the day
We will give thanks and pray to the one.

VERSE 5: — as Verse 1

Hard To Say I'm Sorry

Words & Music by P. Cetera & D. Foster

Love Is All Around

Words & Music by Reg Presley

and so the feel-ing grows.— It's writ-ten on the wind, it's ev-'ry-where I go,— so if you real-ly love me, come on and let it show.—

Verse 2:
I see your face before me
As I lay on my bed;
I cannot get to thinking
Of all the things you said.
You gave your promise to me
And I gave mine to you;
I need someone beside me
In everything I do.

I Will Always Love You

Words & Music by Dolly Parton

Recite:
I hope that life treats you kind,
and I hope you have all that you ever dreamed of,
and I wish you joy and happiness,
but above all this, I wish you love.

Sing:
And I will always love you,
I will always love you,
I will always love you,
And I will always love you,
I will always love you,
I will always love you.

She Loves You

Words & Music by John Lennon & Paul McCartney

Moderately

She loves you, yeh, yeh, yeh. — She loves you, yeh,

yeh, yeh. — She loves you, yeh, yeh, yeh, yeh. —

1. You think you've lost your love? —
(2) said you hurt her so, —
(3) know it's up to you, —

Well, I saw her yes - ter -
She al - most lost her
I think it's on - ly

Sometimes When We Touch

Words & Music by Dan Hill & Barry Mann

ask me if ___ I love ___ you and I choke on my ___ re - ply.

-mance with all ___ its strat - e - gy leaves me batt-ling with ___ my pride.

I'd rath - er hurt ___ you hon - est - ly ___ than mis-some

But through the in - sec - ur - i - ty ___

You

times I'd like ___ to break ___ you and drive you to ___ your knees, _____ at
times I'd like ___ to break ___ through ___ and hold _____ you end - less - ly. ___

D. S. al Coda

And
___ in me ___ sub-sides. ___

rall.

That Ole Devil Called Love

Words & Music by Doris Fisher & Allan Roberts

To All The Girls I've Loved Before

Words & Music by Hal David & Albert Hammond

The First Time Ever I Saw Your Face

Words & Music by Ewan MacColl

57

Verse 2:
The first time ever I kissed your mouth
I felt the earth move in my hand,
Like the trembling heart of a captive bird
That was there at my command, my love,
That was there at my command.

Verse 3:
The first time ever I lay with you
And felt your heart so close to mine,
And I knew our joy would fill the earth
And last till the end of time, my love.
The first time ever I saw your face,
Your face, your face, your face.

Touch Me In The Morning

Words by Ron Miller
Music by Michael Masser

Moderate Ballad, expressively

Touch me in the morn - ing, then just walk a - way.
morn - ing, then just close the ___ door.

We don't have to - mor - row, but we had yes - ter - day. ___
Leave me as you ___ found me, emp - ty like be - fore. ___

Hey! Was - n't it me ___ who said ___ that noth - in' good's gon - na last for - ev - er?
Was - n't it yes - ter - day ___ we used to laugh at the wind be - hind ___ us?

Unchained Melody

Music by Alex North
Words by Hy Zaret

Until It's Time For You To Go

Words & Music by Buffy Sainte-Marie

You're not a dream, you're not an an- gel, you're a man.
dif- f'rent, worlds a - part, we're not the same,

I'm not a queen, I'm a wom- an, take my hand.
we laughed and played at the start like in a game.

We'll make a space in the lives that we'd planned,
You could have stayed out- side my heart but in you came,

dream, you're not an an-gel, you're a man, _____ I'm not a queen, I'm a

dim. poco a poco

wom-an, take my hand. _____ We'll make a space in the lives that we'd

planned, _____ and here we'll stay un-til it's time for ___ you to

molto rit.

go.

a tempo

When You're Young And In Love

Words & Music by Van McCoy

Without You

Words & Music by Peter Ham & Tom Evans

PART TWO

Contents

A Woman In Love

Words & Music by Barry Gibb & Robin Gibb

Always Be My Baby

Words by Mariah Carey
Music by Jermaine Dupri, Mariah Carey & Manuel Seal

Moderately

We were as one, babe for a mo-ment in _____ time. _____
I ain't gon-na cry, _ no, and I won't beg you to _____ stay. _____

F   Bb   Bb/C   C#dim7

You'll al-ways be a part of me.___   I'm part of you in-def-i-nite-ly. ___
by.

Dm7   Am7   Bb   Bb/C

Boy, don't you know you can't es-cape_ me.   Ooh dar-ling, cause you'll al-ways be_ my ba

F   Bb   Bb/C   C#dim7

- by.   And we'll lin - ger on.___   Time can't e-rase a feel-ing this strong.___

Dm7   Am7   Bb   Bb/C

                                                   Repeat and Fa

No way you're ev - er gon - na shake_ me.   Oh dar-ling, 'cause you'll al - ways be_ my ba

90

Bridge Over Troubled Water

Words & Music by Paul Simon

Moderate, not too fast, like a spiritual

When you're wea - ry, — feel - ing — small,
down and out, — When you're on the street,

When tears are in your eyes, — I'll dry them — all;
When eve - ning falls so hard — I will com - fort — you.

Could It Be Magic

Words & Music by Barry Manilow & Adrienne Anderson

Falling Into You

Words & Music by Rick Nowles, Marie-Claire D'Ubalio & Billy Steinberg

falling like a star, finding a be-lief, falling where you are. Fall-ing in-to you, fall-ing in-to you, fall- -ing in-to you, hey.

For The Good Times

Words & Music by Kris Kristofferson

I Am Blessed

Words & Music by Marsha Malamet & Mark Mueller

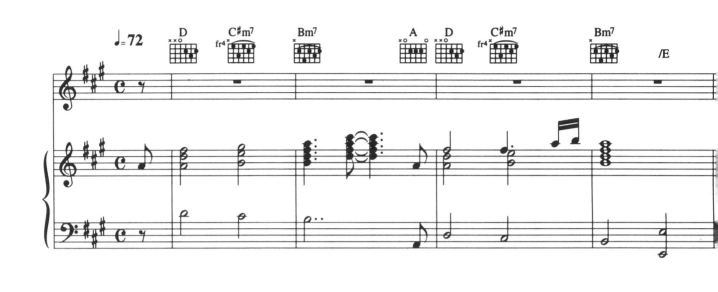

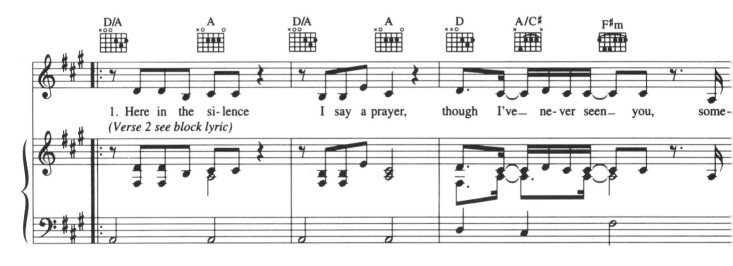

1. Here in the si-lence I say a prayer, though I've ne-ver seen you, some-

(Verse 2 see block lyric)

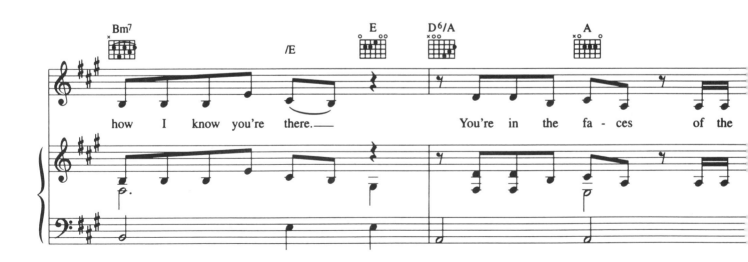

how I know you're there.___ You're in the fa-ces of the

peo - ple that I meet, you're as si - lent as the earth be - neath my

feet. So if I should com - plain, that all I

have is not e - nough for - give me, I've been gi - ven so

much. And I am blessed ev - 'ry

time I look in-to my ba-by's eyes— I think of all— the friends— who've— touched my

life. I re-al-ise in a world where some have more and some have

less, I have love and I am blessed.

love and I am

Verse 2:
So many changes
This world can put you through.
Sometimes it's hard to find a way,
A heart can get confused
But then I hold you and it all falls into place,
You give me what's right and I cannot erase.
So when I'm feeling down
I feel sorry for myself,
I look around and it's easy to tell.

I Can't Stop Loving You

Words & Music by Don Gibson

Those hap-py hours _____ that we once knew _____

— though long a-go _____ they still make me blue. _____

I Write The Songs

Words & Music by Bruce Johnston

1. I've been a-live for-ev-er,
2. My home lies deep with-in you,

and I ___ wrote the ver - y first song.
and I ___ have my own room in your soul.

I put the words and the mel-o-dies ___ to-geth-er, I'm
And we're such good friends when I look out ___ through your win-dows, you make me

Let's Put It All Together

Words & Music by Hugo Perreti, Luigi Creatore, & George David Weiss

Just The Two Of Us

Words & Music by Ralph MacDonald, William Salter & Bill Withers

One Moment In Time

Words & Music by Albert Hammond & John Bettis

This Guy's In Love With You

Words by Hal David
Music by Burt Bacharach

looks at you the way I do?___ When you smile,___

I can tell we know each oth-er ver-y well. How

Steady

can I show you I'm glad I

got to know you, 'cause I've heard___ some talk. They

2nd time fade out within ten measures

The Power Of Love

Words & Music by C. de Rouge, G. Mende, J. Rush & S. Applegate

To Love Somebody

Words & Music by Barry Gibb & Robin Gibb

Un-Break My Heart

Words & Music by Dianne Warren

141

Woman

Words & Music by John Lennon

Moderately slow

When You Tell Me That You Love Me

Words & Music by Albert Hammond & John Bettis

Wonderful Tonight

Words & Music by Eric Clapton

D.S. ⅀ al Coda ⊕

Coda ⊕

Oh, my dar - ling,   you   are

won - der - ful ___ to - night." ___

rit.

Words

Words & Music by Barry Gibb, Robin Gibb & Maurice Gibb

Moderately slow

mp legato

Smile an ev - er - last - ing smile; a smile could bring you

near to me. Don't ev - er let me find you

words, and words are all I have to take your heart a-

way. It's on-ly words, and words are all I

have to take your heart a - way. It's on-ly

words, and words are all I have to take your heart a - way.

rit.

PART THREE

Contents

Ain't No Mountain High Enough

Words & Music by Nickolas Ashford & Valerie Simpson

Verse 2.
I set you free
I told you you could always count on me
From that day on, I made a vow,
I'll be there when you want me,
Some way, some how,
'Cause baby there *(Chorus)*

Verse 3.
My love is alive
Way down in my heart
Although we are miles apart
If you ever need a helping hand,
I'll be there on the double
As fast as I can.
Don't you know that there *(Chorus)*

All I Have To Do Is Dream

Words & Music by Boudleaux Bryant

Moderately

Dream, _____ dream, dream, dream, ___ Dream, _____ dream, dream, dream. ___ When

I want you ___ in my arms, When I want you ___ and all your charms When

I feel blue ___ in the night, And I need you ___ to hold me tight When

An Old Fashioned Love Song

Words & Music by Paul Williams

Annie's Song

Words & Music by John Denver

Eternal Flame

Words & Music by Billy Steinberg, Tom Kelly & Susanna Hoffs

Evergreen

Words by Paul Williams
Music by Barbra Streisand

Feelings (Dime)

By Morris Albert & Louis Gaste

For All We Know

Words by Robb Wilson & Arthur James
Music by Fred Karlin

Love,_____ look at the two of us,_____ Stran-

gers_____ in man-y ways._____ We've got a
Let's take a

life-time__ to share,_____ So much to say_____
life-time__ to say,_____ "I knew you well,"_____

How Deep Is Your Love

Words & Music by Barry Gibb, Robin Gibb & Maurice Gibb

I Feel Fine

Words & Music by John Lennon & Paul McCartney

Moderately

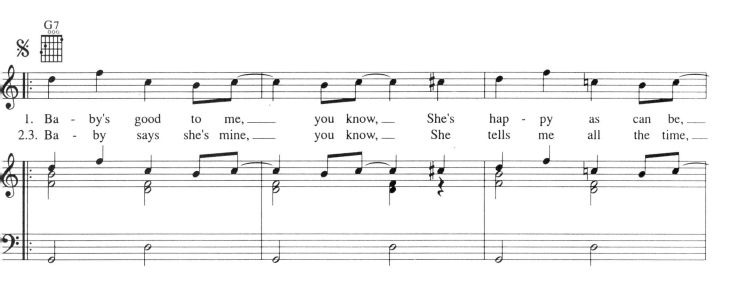

1. Ba - by's good to me, ___ you know, ___ She's hap - py as can be, ___
2.3. Ba - by says she's mine, ___ you know, ___ She tells me all the time, ___

I Will

Words & Music by John Lennon & Paul McCartney

so I can hear you, Make it eas - y to be near you, For the th

you do en-dear you to me, Ah, you know I will.

I will.

La la la la la la la la la la la la la la la.

If You Leave Me Now

Words & Music by Peter Cetera

Jealous Guy

Words & Music by John Lennon

1. I was dream-ing of the past ____
2. I was feel-ing in - se - cure ____
3. (Whistle) .... etc.
4. I was trying to catch your eyes ____

and my heart _ was beat-ing fast ____
you might not love _ me a - ny - more ____
thought that you _ were trying to hide ____

I be-gan _ to lose _ con-trol _
I was shiv - er-ing _ in-side
I was swal - low-ing _ my pain

I be - gan to lose _ con-trol
I was shiv - er-ing _ in - side
I was swal - low-ing _ my pain

Let's Get It On

Words & Music by Marvin Gaye & Ed Townsend

Slow soul beat

mf I've been real-ly try-in', ba-by, try-in' to hold back this feel-

in' for so long. And if you feel like I feel, ba-by,

then come on, oh, come on. Ooh, let's get it on. Ow,

baby, let's get it on. Let's love, baby, let's get it

on. Su-gar, let's get it on. Ooh.

We're all sen-si-tive peo-ple with so much to give, un-der-

Killing Me Softly With His Song

Words by Norman Gimbel
Music by Charles Fox

More Than I Can Say

Words & Music by Sonny Curtis & Jerry Allison

Oh, Pretty Woman

Words & Music by Roy Orbison & Bill Dees

way it must be, O. K._____ I guess I'll go on home it's late There'll be to-mor-row night, but

wait! What do I see_____ Is she walk-ing back to

me?_____ Yeah,___ she's walk-ing back to me!_____

Oh,_____ Pret-ty wo-man_____ Pret-ty wo-man_____

Strangers In The Night

Words by Charles Singleton & Eddie Snyder
Music by Bert Kaempfert

This Is My Song

Words & Music by Charles Chaplin

Barcarolle

Why is my heart so light?

Why are the stars so bright? Why is the sky so blue _____ since the

hour _____ I met you? _____ A - lone I sing in moon - light _____ with

Three Times A Lady

Words & Music by Lionel Richie

(When) we are together
The moments I cherish,
With ev'ry beat of my heart.
To touch you, to hold you
To feel you, to need you.
There's nothing to keep us apart.

Your Song

Words & Music by Elton John and Bernie Taupin

Slow, but with a beat